Something Fishy

Jeanne Willis
Illustrated by Paul Nicholls

R
RIGBY

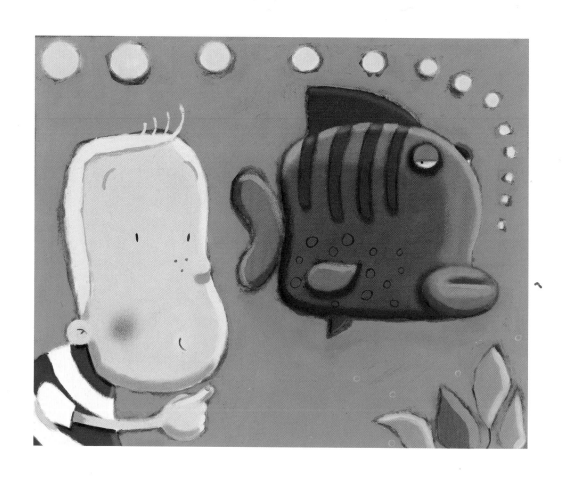

I can see a big fish.

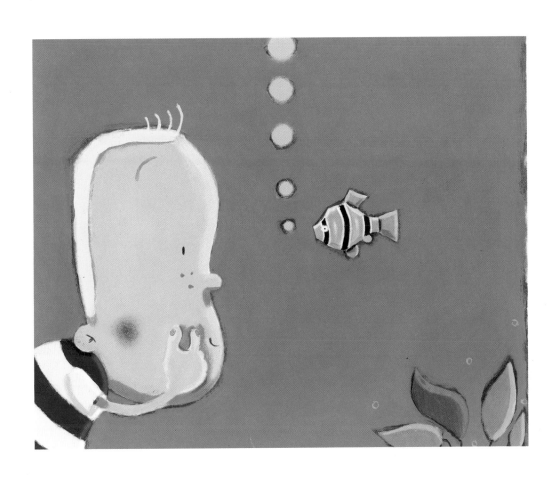

I can see a little fish.

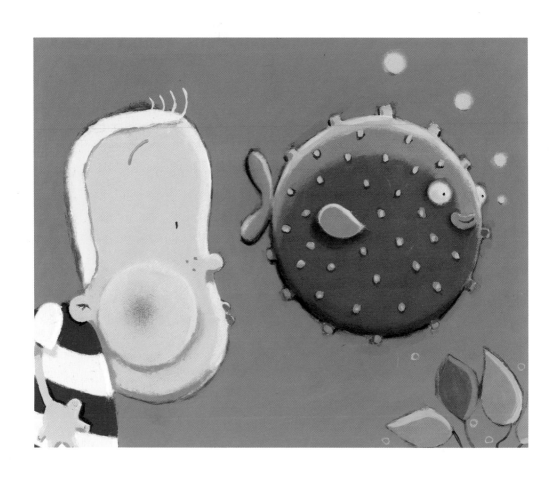

I can see a fat fish.

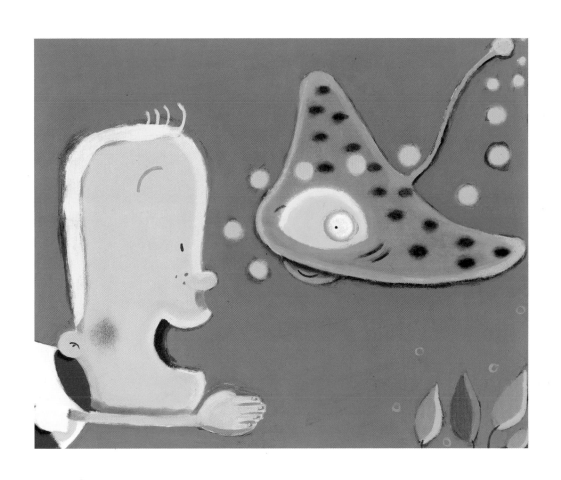

I can see a flat fish.

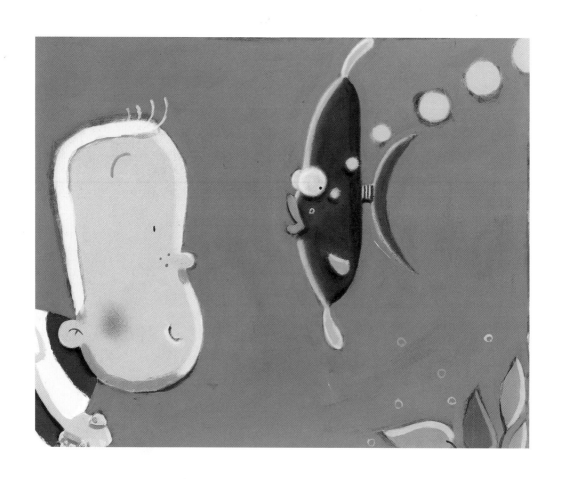

I can see a blue fish.

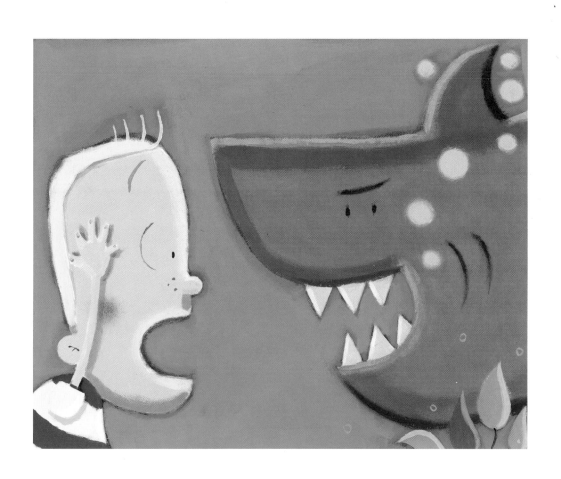

I can see a shark!

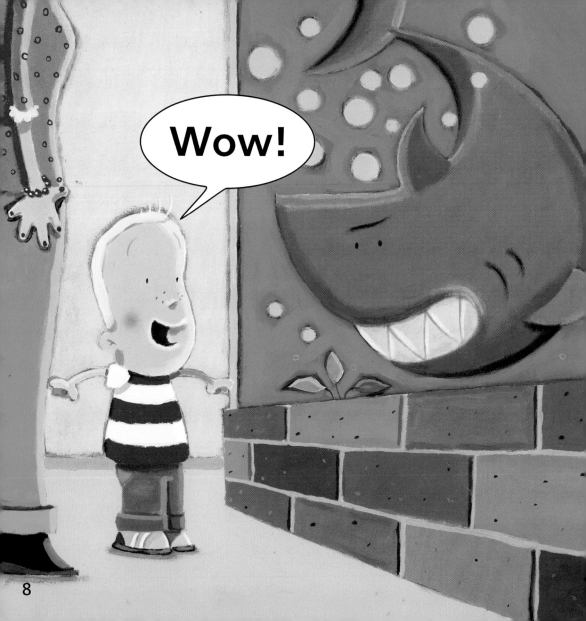